ROADTRIP!™

My Musical Memory Book

Music & Materials by

Jennifer Eklund
&
Kris Skaletski

For the ultimate *Roadtrip!* experience, this book should be used alongside the *Teacher Guidebook & Duets* available at:

PianoPronto.com

PIANO PRONTO PUBLISHING

Roadtrip!™ My Musical Memory Book

Jennifer Eklund & Kris Skaletski

Copyright ©2015 by Piano Pronto Publishing, Inc.

ISBN 978-1-942751-04-05

Printed in the United States of America

Piano Pronto Publishing, Inc.
PianoPronto.com

KiddyKeys®
KiddyKeys.com

Illustrations by Robb Rich
Cover Design by Chaz DeSimone

Draw a picture of your car:

Send a postcard showing your car on the Roadtrip!

Roadtrip! Final Checklist

- ☐ **A pencil and some crayons**

- ☐ **My swimsuit for swimming in the lake**

- ☐ **A healthy snack for the backseat**

- ☐ **My thinking cap**

- ☐ **My favorite piano book**

The adventure begins...

1. The Roadtrip! Song

I'll use gentle touches when I press the keys,
My arms floating up like a leaf in the breeze.

Musical road signs will show us the way.
So pack up your things and let's hit the highway!

Rules of the Road
RIGHT HAND & LEFT HAND

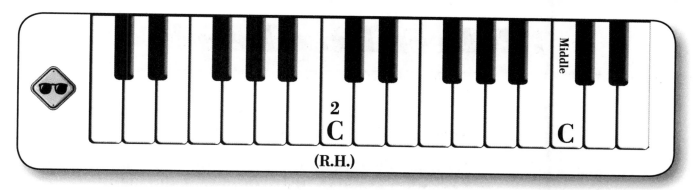

(R.H.)

1. The Roadtrip! Song

(Melody: "The Farmer in the Dell")

Joyfully
Play one octave lower

Traditional
Lyrics by Kris Skaletski

What did you see on the first part of your roadtrip?

The adventure continues...

2. Beep Beep Beep!

Start off on the road that goes high and goes low.
Sometimes we'll go fast and sometimes we'll go slow.

We'll say beep beep beep as we play through this song.
Let's do it together. Let's all sing along!

Rules of the Road
FINGER NUMBERS

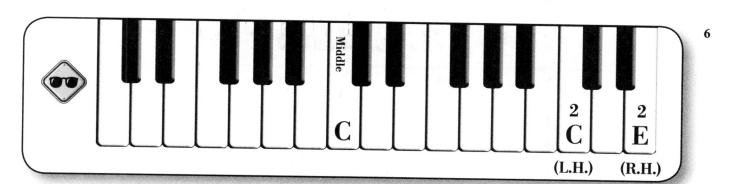

2. Beep Beep Beep!

Jennifer Eklund
Lyrics by Kris Skaletski

Quickly
Play as written

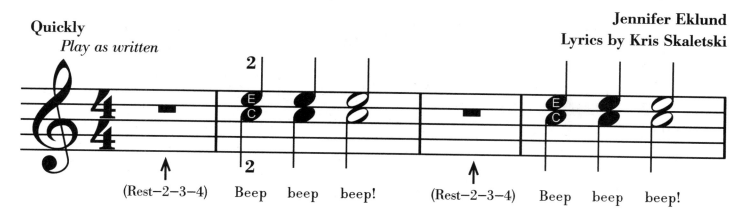

(Rest–2–3–4)   Beep   beep   beep!   (Rest–2–3–4)   Beep   beep   beep!

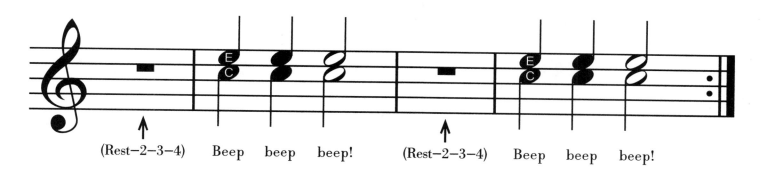

(Rest–2–3–4)   Beep   beep   beep!   (Rest–2–3–4)   Beep   beep   beep!

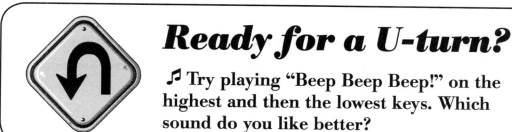

Ready for a U-turn?

♫ Try playing "Beep Beep Beep!" on the highest and then the lowest keys. Which sound do you like better?

♫ *"Beep Beep Beep!" is a happy-sounding song. Color the car below a happy color.*

The adventure continues...

3. Lullaby

Play the keys fast and *Allegro* you'll go,
Play the keys slow and the tempo's *Lento*.

The next song for you has a tempo to keep.
Lento is the tempo, but don't fall asleep!

Rules of the Road
READ TO THE RIGHT

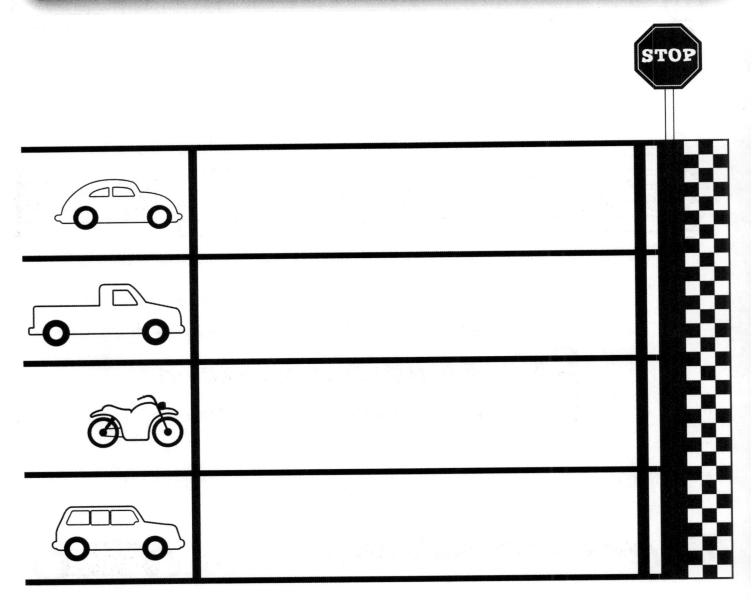

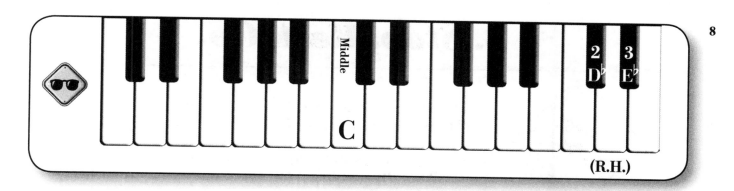

3. Lullaby

Jennifer Eklund
Lyrics by Kris Skaletski

Lento
Play one octave higher

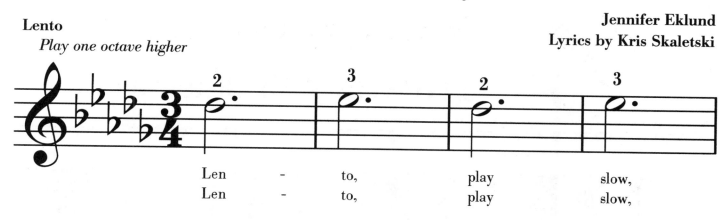

Len - to, play slow,
Len - to, play play slow,

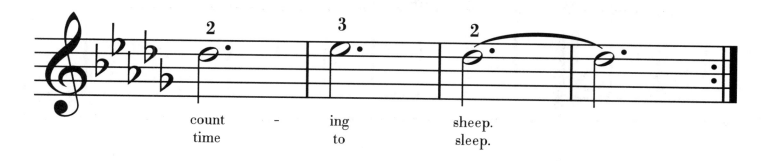

count - ing sheep.
time to sleep.

Ready for a U-turn?

♫ Play "Lullaby" Allegro (fast). Does the song still sound like a lullaby?

The adventure continues...

4. Stop, Rest, Go!

Do you need a rest? Sometimes I do too!
A rest sign's ahead and it's something new.

Go from the beginning and stop at the end.
Between you'll see rests. Do your best now, my friend.

Rules of the Road
FIND C BY TWO BLACK KEYS

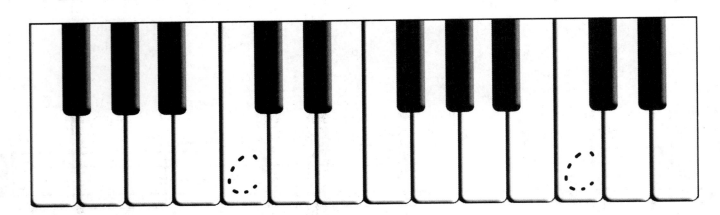

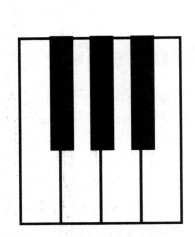

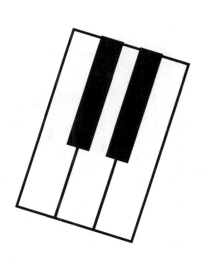

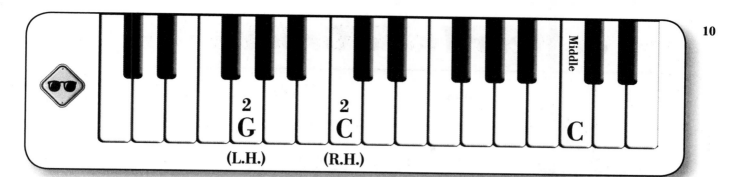

4. Stop, Rest, Go!

(Melody: "Do Your Ears Hang Low?")

Allegro
Play one octave lower

Traditional
Lyrics by Kris Skaletski

What did you learn about on the Roadtrip! today?

The adventure continues...

5. Merrily We Groove Along

Are you feelin' groovy? Are you feelin' fine?
Do you play the piano, all of the time?

Three keys that are black we'll be playing today.
The black keys are fun, let's go play them, hooray!

Rules of the Road
FIND GROUPS OF THREE BLACK KEYS

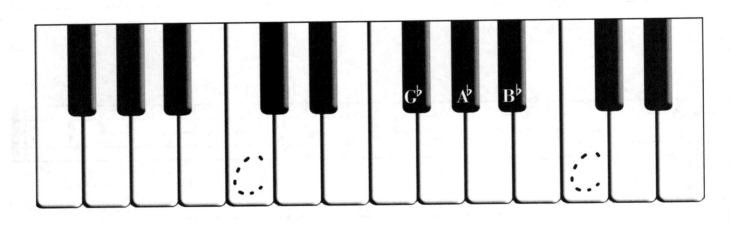

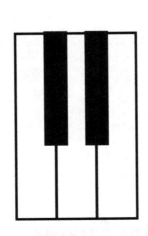

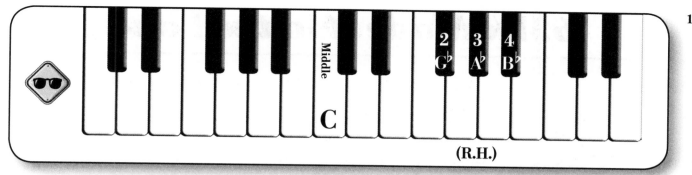

5. Merrily We Groove Along

(Melody: "Mary Had a Little Lamb")

Groovin'
Play one octave higher

Traditional
Lyrics by Kris Skaletski

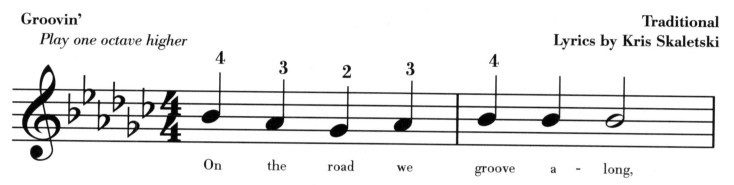

On the road we groove a - long,

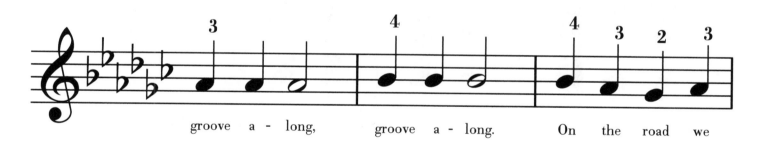

groove a - long, groove a - long. On the road we

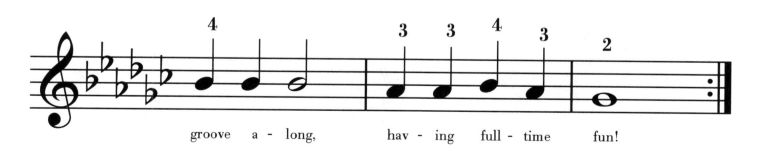

groove a - long, hav - ing full - time fun!

♫ *Yellow can be a full-time fun color. Color the car in with a color you think is fun!*

The adventure continues...

6. We Made it to the Lake!

You've made it so far, and you're doing so great!
The sound of your playing is really first rate.

Remember your arms, like they float in the breeze.
Count 1, 2, 3, 4 and you'll do it with ease.

Play piano, play forte, play high and play low.
We read left to right when we play pi-a-no.

You've reached the next stop, so go have some fun.
Your roadtrip adventure has only begun!

Rules of the Road

FIND D NEXT DOOR TO C

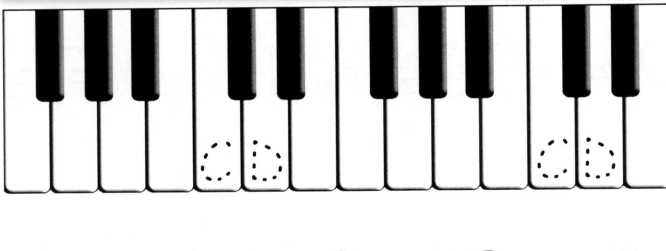

C P C R D

E R D F

D C L C X

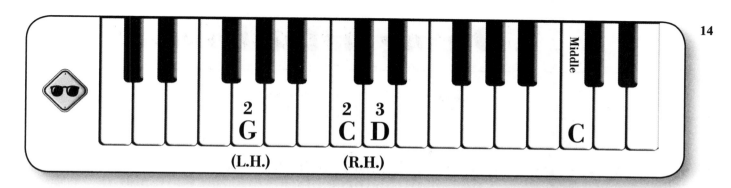

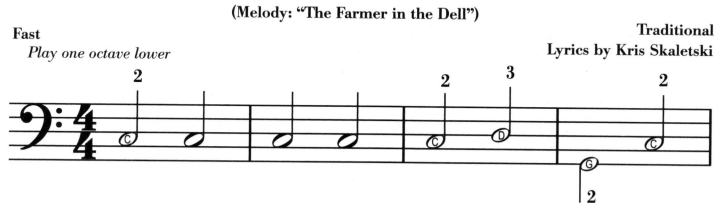

6. We Made it to the Lake!

(Melody: "The Farmer in the Dell")

Fast
Play one octave lower

Traditional
Lyrics by Kris Skaletski

Draw a picture of what you see at the lake.

The adventure continues...

7. Diving in the Lake

We're here at the spot where you'll have lots of fun.
Dive into this song, then we'll say "well done!"

Curve all of your fingers while pressing the keys.
Come play the three black keys, flat G, A, and B.

Rules of the Road
QUARTER, HALF, & WHOLE NOTES

1–2

1–2–3–4

1

Color me in!

1

Color me in!

1–2

1–2–3–4

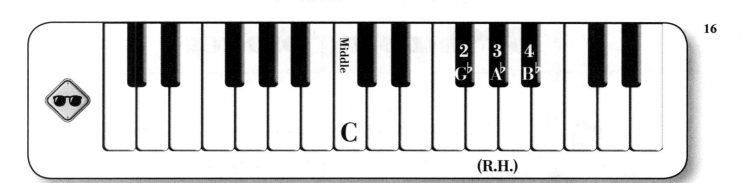

7. Diving in the Lake

(Melody: "Old MacDonald")

Traditional
Lyrics by Kris Skaletski

Happily
Play one octave higher

Full - time fun can now be - gin. 4 4 3 3 2

I am read - y to dive in. 4 4 3 3 2

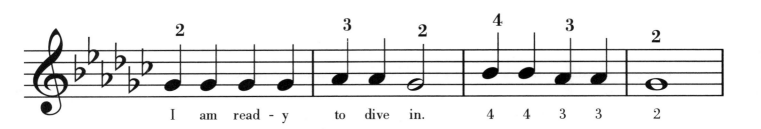

To the lake, to the lake, to to to to the lake!

Through the air I jumped so far, div - ing in the lake!

The adventure continues...

8. Skipping Stones

Today we'll have fun as we skip all around.
We'll skip on the keys and we'll skip on the ground.

Get your right hand ready, it's time now to play.
Let's go skip around on the white keys today.

Rules of the Road

SKIPS ON THE STAFF

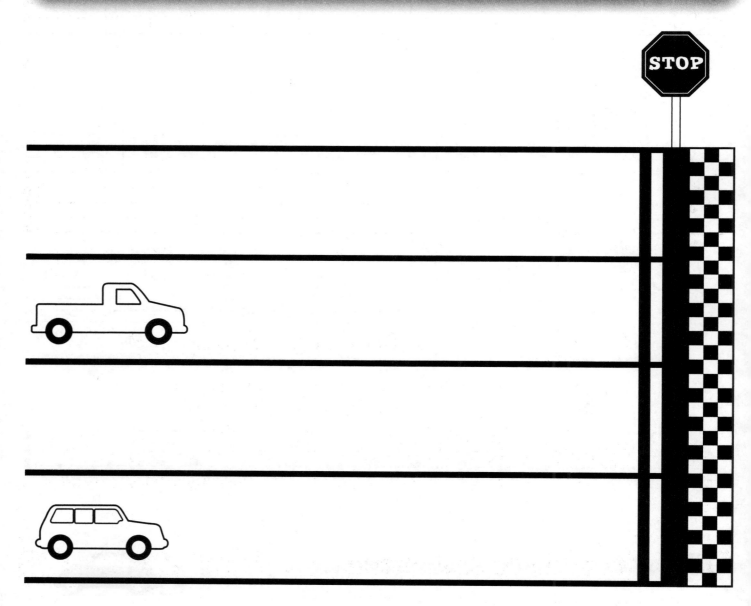

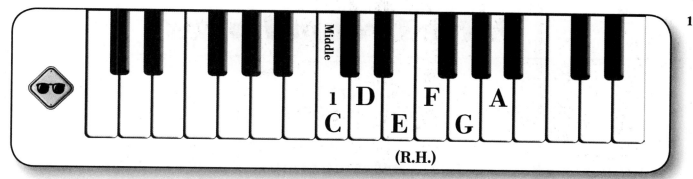

🎹 8. Skipping Stones

Jennifer Eklund
Lyrics by Kris Skaletski

Joyfully
Play two octaves higher

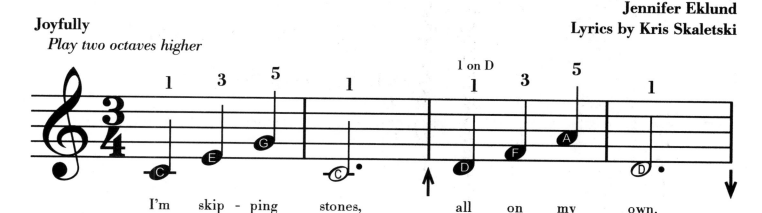

I'm skip - ping stones, all on my own.

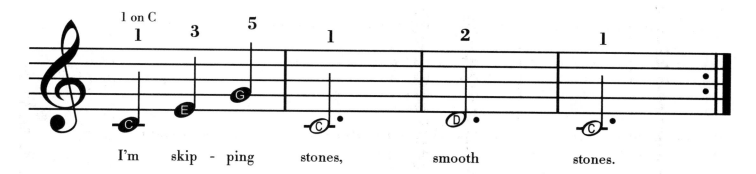

I'm skip - ping stones, smooth stones.

Ready for a U-turn?

🎵 Move your thumb to G and play this song again using the finger numbers shown. Which way do you prefer?

🎵 *Choose a rainbow of colors for the car. Pick any colors you like–it's your choice!*

The adventure continues...

9. Ice Cream Party!

This song is a treat, it's one you'll like to play.
It's all about ice cream, and taste it you may.

When you are all done you might just take a bow.
Right hand at the ready, let's go learn it now!

Rules of the Road
FINGER NUMBER REVIEW

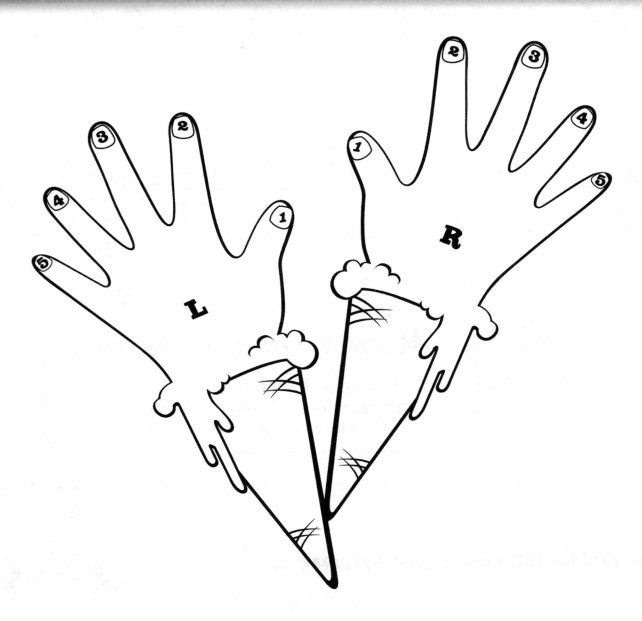

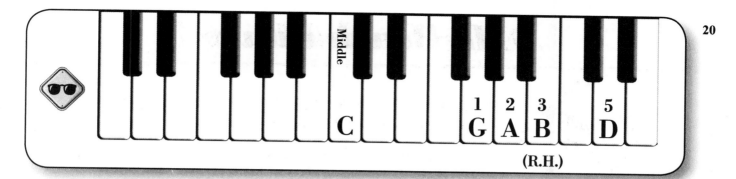

9. Ice Cream Party!

Happily
Play one octave higher

Jennifer Eklund
Lyrics by Kris Skaletski

Goin' to get some ice cream! It's time for a treat!

Goin' to get some ice cream! Ice cream can't be beat!

Draw a picture of your favorite type of ice cream.

The adventure continues...

10. Beach Bunny

Can you hop like a bunny, can you hop all around?
We look up and down and there are notes to be found.

Play quarter and half notes, one beat and then two.
We finish the song with a trick just for you!

Rules of the Road
MUSIC ALPHABET SEARCH

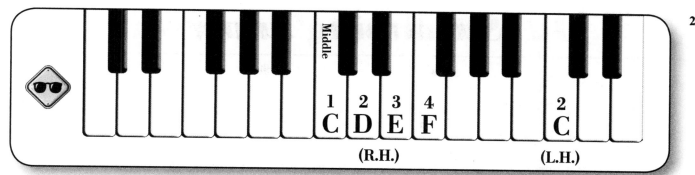

10. Beach Bunny

(Melody: "B-I-N-G-O")

Joyfully
Play two octaves higher

Traditional
Lyrics by Kris Skaletski

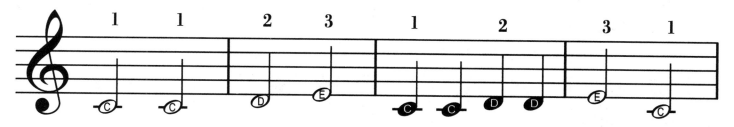

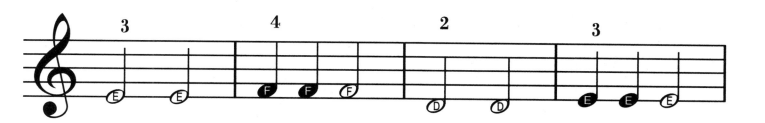

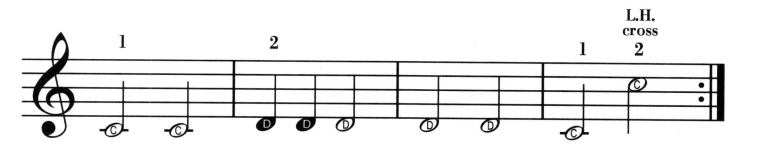

The adventure continues...

11. Swimming Superstar

Get ready to use left and right hand today.
Black keys and a white one we're going to play.

A beautiful melody known near and far.
This song is a favorite, it shines like a star.

Rules of the Road
LINES & SPACES ON THE STAFF

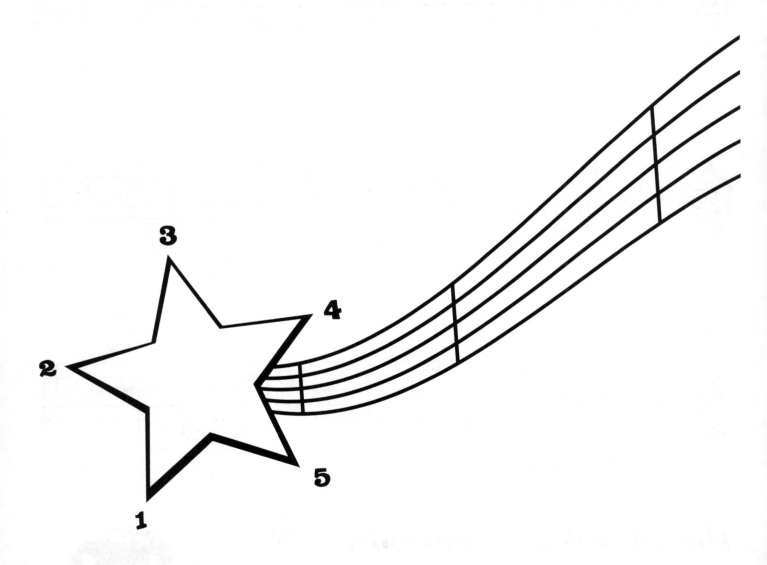

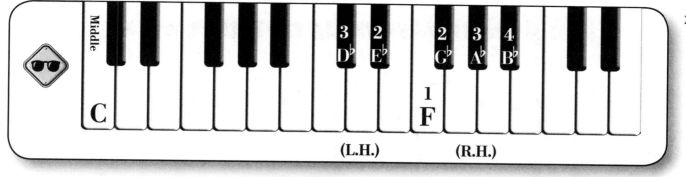

11. Swimming Superstar

(Melody: "Twinkle, Twinkle, Little Star")

Traditional
Lyrics by Kris Skaletski

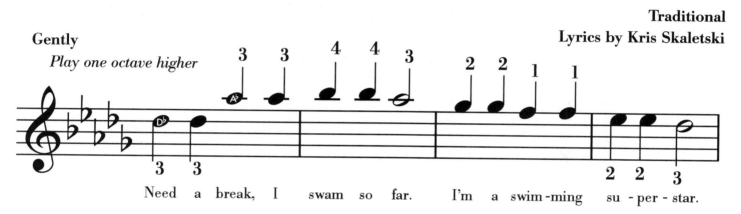

Need a break, I swam so far. I'm a swim-ming su-per-star.

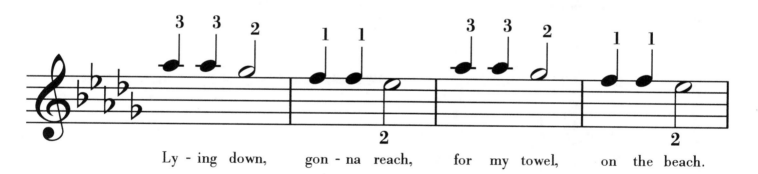

Ly-ing down, gon-na reach, for my towel, on the beach.

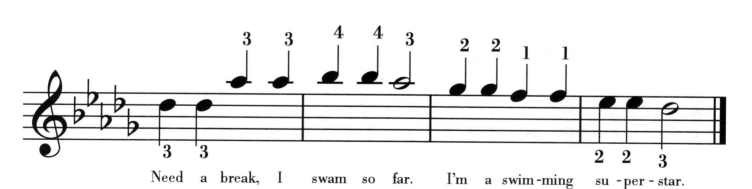

Need a break, I swam so far. I'm a swim-ming su-per-star.

The adventure continues...

This roadtrip is a-maze-ing!

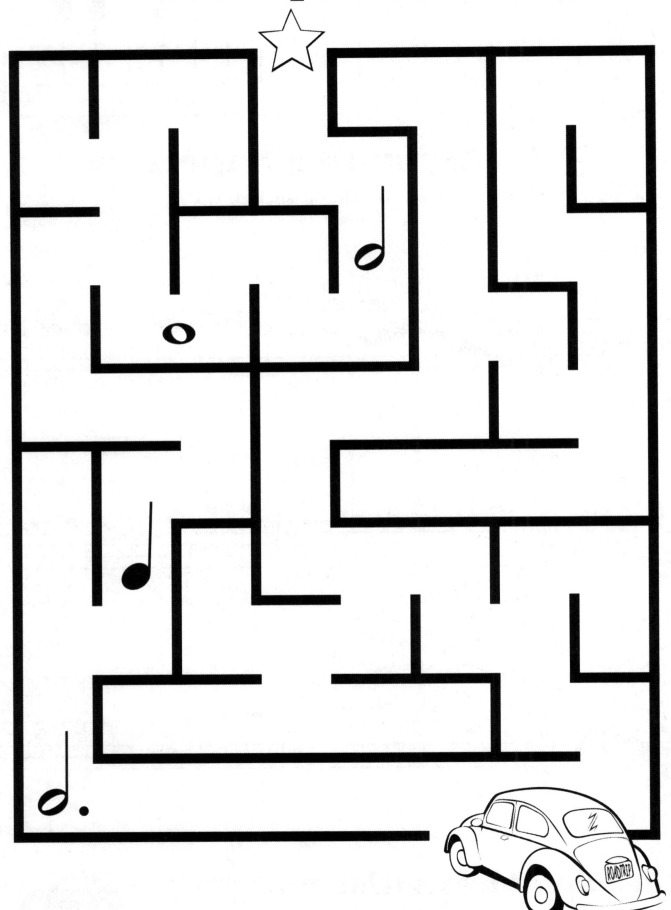

My colorful day at the lake...

12. It's Time to Go

We're learning our notes and it's easy to see,
The notes in the piece are C-D-E-G.

We use lots of fingers but won't use the 4.
Repeat at the end means we'll go back for more.

Rules of the Road
FORGET THE 4

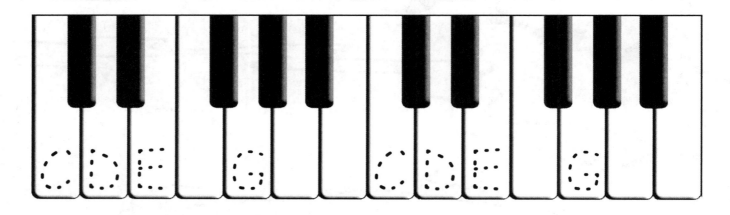

1   4   2   3   5

3   5   2   4

4   1   4   5   1

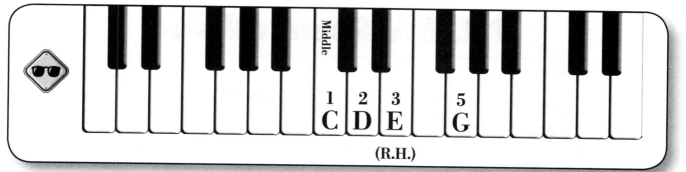

12. It's Time to Go

Joyfully
Play two octaves higher

Jennifer Eklund
Lyrics by Kris Skaletski

It's time to go, back on the road.

We had our fun lake - side.

I'm on my way, play - ing to - day.

Back on the road now.

The adventure continues...

13. Backseat Blues

This song has a flat sign and that's something new.
It looks kind of different, does it sound sad to you?

Use 3 on the E-flat, that's what you should do.
Three notes in this song, so let's start now on cue.

Rules of the Road
FIND THE FLAT SIGNS

♫ *What's your favorite snack?* _____

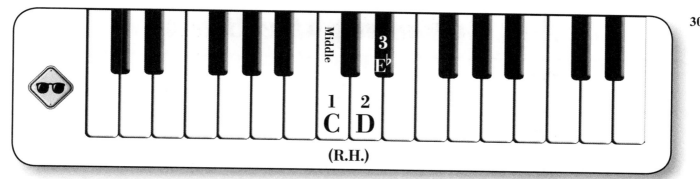

13. Backseat Blues

Jennifer Eklund
Lyrics by Kris Skaletski

Sadly
Play two octaves higher

Back - seat blues. Lost my shoe. Need a snack and

'I can't choose. Back - seat blues. Where's my shoe?

I might need a nap! How long till we're back?

♪ *There are many different shades of blue. Color the car your favorite shade of blue.*

The adventure continues...

14. Crossing the Bridge

Remember that trick when you crossed to the C?
Do that a whole bunch and a rockstar you'll be.

Play three easy notes, keep on going, don't stop.
Then 2 crosses over, press C at the top.

Rules of the Road
THE MUSIC ALPHABET

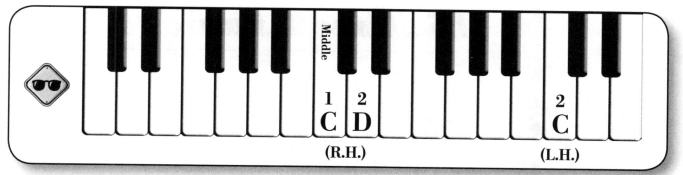

14. Crossing the Bridge

(Melody: "London Bridge")

Carefully
Play one octave higher

Traditional
Lyrics by Kris Skaletski

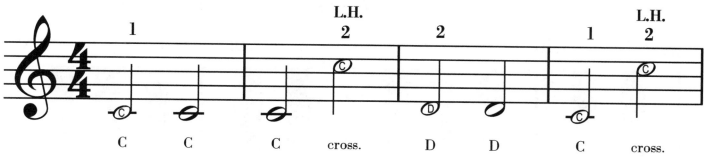

C   C   C   cross.   D   D   C   cross.

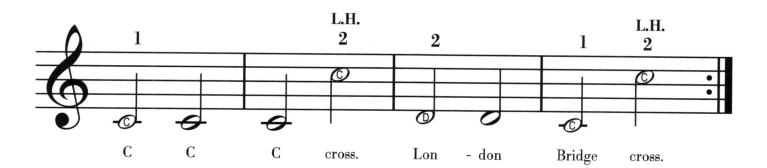

C   C   C   cross.   Lon - don   Bridge   cross.

Ready for a U-turn?

🎵 Play "Crossing the Bridge" again, this time crossing over two C's higher up on the keyboard. Which do you like better?

The adventure continues...

15. Time 4 Fun

These are the notes that you'll play for me.
G–A–B–D and G–A–B–C.

It's full-time fun, to step up to 4.
It's full-time fun, let's go have some more!

Rules of the Road
FIND G, A, B, C, & D

Color me in!

1–2–3

Color me in!

1–2–3

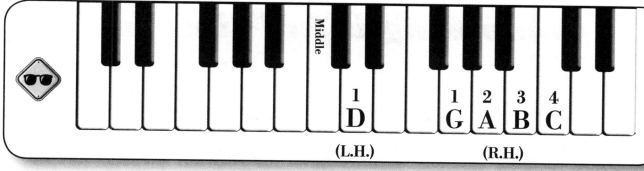

15. Time 4 Fun

Proudly
Play two octaves higher

Jennifer Eklund
Lyrics by Kris Skaletski

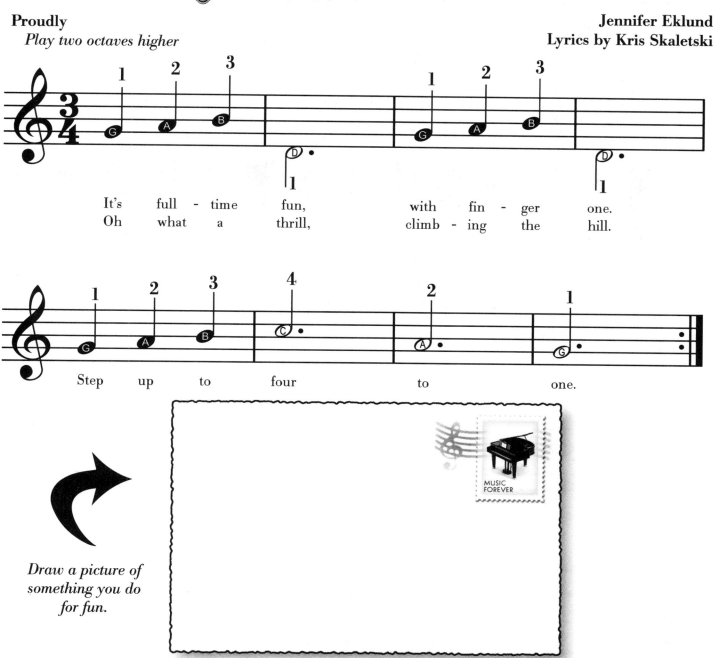

It's full - time fun, with fin - ger one.
Oh what a thrill, climb - ing the hill.

Step up to four to one.

Draw a picture of something you do for fun.

The adventure continues...

Composing is full-time fun!

♪ *Choose three musical bits below. Your teacher will help you add them to the staff.*

(Title)

(Tempo)

(Composer)

Now let's make a spooky song...

♫ Choose three musical bits below. Your teacher will help you add them to the staff.

(Title)

(Tempo)

(Composer)

16. I See (C) Cars

I see, do you see, the key that we call C?
Find the two black keys and go left from D.

C is for car, and for cat, and for cow,
Look for two black keys and you will know how.

Rules of the Road
C WORDS & KEY REVIEW

♫ *What's your favorite animal?* _____

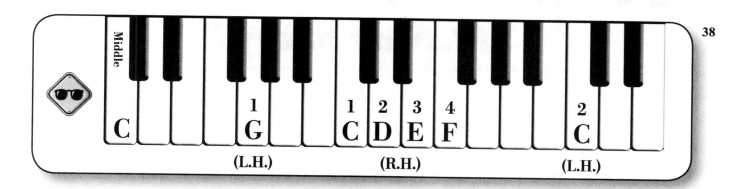

16. I See (C) Cars

Joyfully
Play one octave higher

Jennifer Eklund
Lyrics by Kris Skaletski

I see cars. They pass me by. I like to wave "hi!"

Bus - es, trucks, and camp - ers too, out my win - dow view.

Red and blue and green and black, like we're on a race - track.

The adventure continues...

39

17. Stay Sharp!

You're sharp! Work hard! Keep doing your best!
Keep reading the notes and continue your quest.

Eyes up on the page, left to right, you'll go far.
Watch where you are going, and you'll be a star!

Rules of the Road
FIND THE SHARP SIGNS

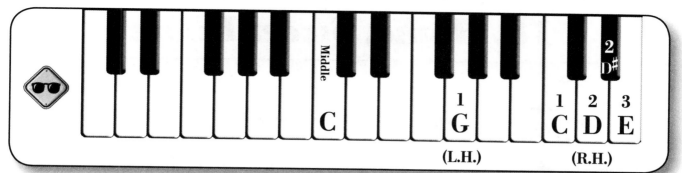

17. Stay Sharp!

Joyfully
Play one octave higher

Jennifer Eklund
Lyrics by Kris Skaletski

The adventure continues...

18. Home, Sweet Home

This is your last song,
But not your last poem.

We're glad to have gone,
But there's no place like home.

Rules of the Road
FINAL NOTE REVIEW

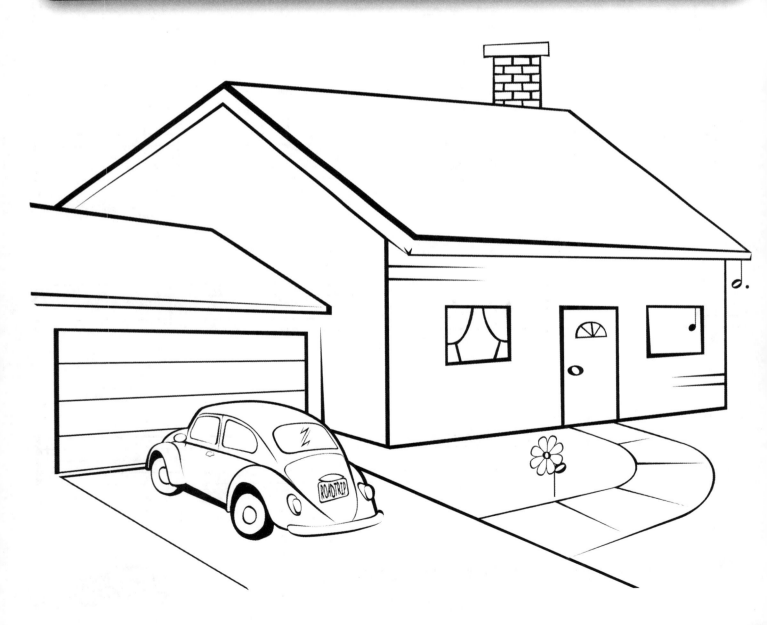

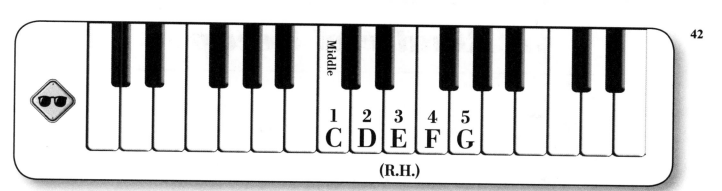

(R.H.)

18. Home, Sweet Home

(Melody: "The Farmer in the Dell")

Allegro
Play one octave higher

Traditional
Lyrics by Kris Skaletski

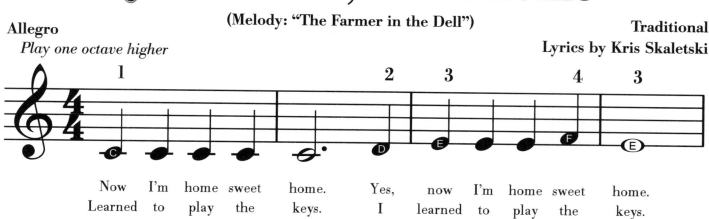

| Now | I'm | home | sweet | home. | Yes, | now | I'm | home | sweet | home. |
| Learned | to | play | the | keys. | I | now | learned | to | play | the | keys. |

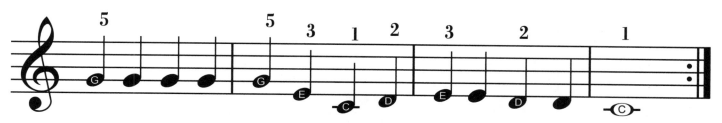

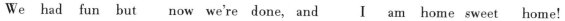

We had fun but now we're done, and I am home sweet home!

Draw a picture of your home.

The adventure continues...

Roadtrip! Recap

Our roadtrip is over, we've come to the end.
We've had a great time, you've done well now, my friend.

The adventure continues, there's still more to learn.
But this trip is over, it's time to adjourn.

My three favorite Roadtrip! songs:

1. _____

2. _____

3. _____

License Plate Game

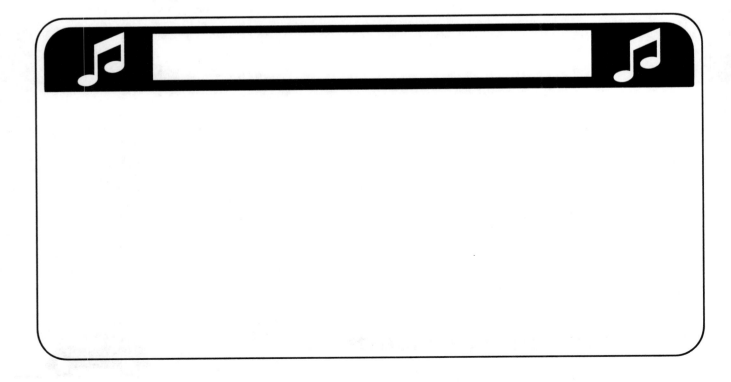

My favorite Roadtrip! activity was:

Where I want to go on my next trip:

Until next time...